STEPHANIDES BROTHERS'
# GREEK MYTHOLOGY

**SERIES B: GODS AND MEN          No. 12**

# E U R O P A

Retold by MENELAOS STEPHANIDES
Illustrated by YANNIS STEPHANIDES

Translation BRUCE WALTER

**SIGMA PUBLICATIONS**
20, MAVROMIHALI ST., 106 80 ATHENS, TEL: +30 210 3607667, FAX: +30 210 3638941

**www.sigmabooks.gr**
e-mail: sbooks@otenet.gr

EUROPA

1st edition 1982
6th edition revised 2003

Supervised by Dimidris Stephanides
Printed by "Fotolio", bound by Dedes Dionysis and Co.

Published and printed in Greece.

ISBN: 960-425-026-4

# EUROPA AND CADMUS

In those distant days, there reigned in the East, in fabled Sidon, a king named Agenor, son of the earth-shaker Poseidon and the Oceanid Libya. Agenor had three sons: Phoenix, Cilix and Cadmus, and a daughter, Europa, who was so lovely that even the goddess Aphrodite was envious of her beauty.

**AN EVIL DREAM**

One night, Europa dreamed that two women were struggling bitterly for her possession. One was called the East and the other the West. If the East won, Europa would remain in her birthplace among her own people, but if the West were the victor, then she would leave with her on a long voyage beyond the blue sea to the regions where the sun sets in majesty each night.

It was the West who won that struggle. Torn with grief, the East was obliged to bid farewell to the lovely princess her soil had borne and raised, and whose dazzling beauty was the pride of all Asia.

Europa woke in terror, for nothing in the world would induce her to leave the land that had given her birth and the parents she loved so deeply. Kneeling in prayer, she begged the gods, and above all Zeus, to save her from exile and the loss of her dear ones.

But Zeus had other plans for the girl. It was he who had sent the god of dreams to trouble her sleep, for he had wished her to come willingly to the West, and he was far from pleased when he saw that Europa shuddered at the very thought of leaving home. Be that as it may, mighty Zeus was stirred by the desire to bring the lovely princess to Greece and make her his wife, and what Zeus wished had to be accomplished. Now

that Oneiros, god of dreams, had failed him he contrived a secret plan to carry off the unsuspecting maiden.

One sunny spring day, Europa and her friends went out with baskets to gather flowers and enjoy the beauty of the countryside. Dancing and skipping for joy, they came to a flowery meadow and soon made it echo with their happy cries and songs. Before them stretched the boundless sea, calm and inviting, while in a green field nearby the herds of Europa's father, king Agenor, stood grazing.

The princess laughed and played with her friends, running from flower to flower as happily as a lark. She wore a charming red dress and her face was radiant with the delight of sharing such surroundings with companions she loved. The breeze caressed her silken hair and the golden rays of the sun bathed it in their glory, making her lovely face more beautiful still.

As they were playing, a handsome white bull ambled away from Agenor's herd and slowly made its way towards Europa. The splendid beast drew the princess' attention like a magnet, gazing at her with its great, expressive eyes as if in admiration. And all the while it drew gradually closer, gambolling playfully as if it were seeking her company. It was an animal of astonishing beauty. Its snowy-white hide, unusual in a bull, gave it an air of added majesty. A black band on its forehead set off its white head to perfection, while its widespread horns, shining like two half moons of precious stone, were the crowning glory of this superb creature. And on its breath there was the sweet smell of ambrosia.

But it was not only the beauty and the noble appearance of the bull which captured Europa's attention. It was also so clearly friendly. In fact, it seemed so gentle and harmless that Europa did not hesitate to walk towards it in her turn and caress its mas-

sive neck. And then she called out to her friends to come and admire the magnificent animal. Not even in the herds of the gods could there be another creature like this!

Europa and the bull were soon firm friends. Taking great care not to harm her, the gentle animal played with the lovely princess and finally went down on its knees, inviting her to climb up and ride. Without hesitation, Europa gaily mounted its broad, velvety back. Delighted, the bull began to play again, trotting in and out among Europa's laughing companions. With light and gambolling steps it made its way towards the sea, with Europa waving her hand and her friends responding with a laughing mock farewell. But this farewell, intended in jest, was soon to prove all too real. For a moment later the bull quickened its pace and drew away from the group of girls. Europa was now becoming anxious and wanted to get down, but this was no longer possible, for the bull had broken into a gallop, and seconds later it charged into the sea. Terror-stricken, the lovely maiden clung to the beast's horns and cried out desperately for help. But it was already too late: swimming with speed and grace the bull drew further and further away from the shore, bearing on its back the princess it had so cunningly carried off. For the bull was none other than Zeus himself, who had wrought this transformation to deceive the lovely daughter of Agenor and spirit her away to the land of the setting sun.

Their progress to the West was stately and triumphant. Poseidon, the brother of Zeus, who rules over the sea, cast down his magic trident on the waves, commanding the waters to be still and not wet so much as the hem of Europa's dress. With his wife Amphitrite at his side, he rode behind the bull Zeus and Europa in a golden chariot drawn by four prancing sea horses. A host of nereids followed in the sea god's wake, while on both sides dolphins plunged and jumped in joy and seabirds wheeled over-

**EUROPA IS CARRIED OFF**

head. And heading the procession went his son, young Triton, blowing triumphant peals on a great conch horn to herald the coming of Agenor's daughter to the West. But she, poor girl, knew nothing of what all this meant and clung in fear to the bull's back, remembering with longing her home and her dear ones and wondering whether she would ever see them again.

And in this way they arrived in Crete. Ever since that day, Crete and Greece and the whole of the continent which lies to the West, as far as the great ocean, have borne the name of Europa, the lovely maiden who came from the East against her will.

**EUROPA
IN CRETE**

In the cave of Dicte, hidden high among the Cretan mountains, the Four Seasons made ready the bridal bed for Zeus' beloved. The Three Graces sprinkled the fragrance of beauty upon her and combed her silken hair until there was no woman in the world could rival the loveliness of Europa. When all was ready, Zeus, now transformed into an eagle, was united with her at last. From this sacred union were born three sons: Minos, the fabled ruler of Crete, Rhadamanthys, the wise law-maker, and Sarpedon, the first king of Lycia.

Zeus presented Europa with many rich gifts. Among them were Laelaps, a hunting dog which never let its prey escape and a golden bow with magic arrows which always hit their mark. But Zeus' constant fear was that Europa might leave Crete or be found by her father Agenor and taken back to the East. To guard against such a possibility he set the terrible giant Talos to keep watch over the island.

Talos was no ordinary giant. He had neither mother nor father, but was the crea-

## THE GIANT TALOS

tion of Hephaestus, master-craftsman of the gods, who had forged him from solid bronze and then breathed life and fearsome strength into his body. Talos was invincible: neither arrow, spear nor sword could pierce his brazen flanks. And he was not only invincible but immortal. For magic blood which gave him everlasting life coursed through his frame in veins of bronze. Hephaestus had sealed it inside his body with a golden plug set in his right foot.

The giant mounted guard over Crete both night and day, patrolling the island watchfully and shaking the regions he passed through with the thud of his heavy footsteps. No foreign ship would approach the great island for fear that the terrible giant might hurl a mighty rock and sink it in an instant.

Talos' awe-inspiring strength served as protection not only for Zeus' beloved, the fair Europa, but for the whole of Crete. Wealthy though the island might be, no would-be conqueror even dared think of setting foot on it.

Talos, of course, was a figment of men's imagination. But even so this myth, like many others, holds a grain of truth. It is indeed true that Crete feared no invader in those days; the island empire was so mighty that its cities had neither walls nor fortresses to guard them. While the story may have had it that the fearsome giant Talos guarded the island, it was a giant of another, but equally impressive kind which really performed that task: the Cretan people and their powerful fleet. And when, with the passing of time, the power of Crete began to wane, so the myth took shape. It is said that Talos was killed by the Argonauts, or rather by their leader, Jason, with the help of his wife, Medea. She made the giant tipsy with wine and Jason pulled out the golden plug which held the magic blood in his veins. It came gushing out and Talos became a lifeless statue of bronze; and ever afterwards, all those who looked on it remembered the lost majesty of Crete and were silent.

But the myth of Europa has another chapter.

When king Agenor learned that his daughter had been carried off, he was almost beside himself with grief and determined to do whatever lay in his power to find the girl and bring her back. So he called his three sons, Phoenix, Cilix and Cadmus and told them:

**THE SONS OF AGENOR SEARCH FOR EUROPA**

"Listen to what I command. The anguish I feel for my beloved daughter is more than my heart can bear. Only if she is found again shall I find peace. You are young and strong. Go, and search everywhere. Scour the whole world until you find Europa and bring her back to me. But do not dare to return without your sister – for if you come back empty-handed I shall give you cause to regret it."

And so Agenor's three sons took their most devoted servants and went in search of Europa, each one taking a different road.

Phoenix set off towards the south, but it was a blind and fruitless search and he soon lost hope and abandoned the effort. Because he was afraid to return to his father without Europa, he stayed where his wanderings had brought him and ruled over a land which ever since has been called Phoenicia.

The same future lay in store for Cilix, who had struck out northwards. He too remained and became king of the country which took his name: Cilicia.

But Agenor's youngest son was of a far different mettle from his brothers. For him, a father's command was a sacred bond. Cadmus had a strength and courage not given to common men, and he was determined to achieve the impossible if by so doing his sister could be reunited with her family. Yet how was he to know that Zeus himself was keeping Europa hidden away, and that all his efforts were thus doomed to failure from the start?

Cadmus and his little band of faithful followers boarded a ship and set off towards the West. They had been sailing for some days when they finally made out the mountains of Crete in the distance. **CADMUS**

"We must go ashore here and begin our search," said Cadmus.

"We cannot even approach this island," was the captain's reply. "A fearsome giant guards it by night and day. As soon as he sets eyes on a foreign ship he throws half a mountainside at it and smashes it to driftwood and by the same reasoning, I don't see how Europa could have landed on Crete. No, it is elsewhere that our search must begin."

And so they left behind them the island where, had they but known it, Europa lay concealed and continued their voyage until they made landfall in Greece.

There, Cadmus went from city to city asking after his sister, but he heard not a single word that might lead to her whereabouts until somebody told him:

"Only Pythia the seer can tell you where Europa is hidden. Go to the Oracle of Apollo at Delphi, and if you learn nothing there, then you must resign yourself to the fact that you will never see her again."

A few days later Cadmus reached Delphi and asked where and how he could find his sister. The answer the oracle gave him was as follows:

"Son of Agenor, give up your vain search for Europa, for you will never find her anywhere. But in the morning, as soon as rosy-fingered Dawn appears in the heavens, go instead and seek the cattle of king Pelagon. There in his herd you will find a cow marked with the sign of the moon on each flank. Let that beast be your guide, and when it is weary from its wanderings and sinks to the ground, then offer it in sacrifice to Mother Earth and sprinkle its blood on the soil of your new homeland. For in that place you will build a mighty fortress which you will call Cadmea, and at its feet a city with wide streets which shall be named Thebes."

When Cadmus received this reply he realized that it was the will of the gods that he should never find Europa and so next morning at daybreak he set out in search of the animal Pythia had told him of. It did not take him long to find the herd of king Pelagon, and among the cows there stood out one with a moon-shaped mark on each flank. As if it knew what it must do, the beast began to walk away, and Cadmus followed it. The animal made its way eastwards, crossing the whole province of Phocis without stopping to rest, and then made its way into the region named Boeotia where it finally lay down on the grass, exhausted.

Then Cadmus thanked Apollo for the help his oracle had given, kissed the soil of

his new homeland, and together with his followers built an altar to sacrifice the sacred beast to Mother Earth. But there was no water for the sacrifice, and so he sent his servants in search of some.

His men soon found a spring in a cave and began to fill their flasks. But suddenly a huge and hideous dragon darted out of a cleft in the rock, plunged its ugly head into their midst and tore them all to pieces.

Cadmus awaited their return in vain. Eventually, following their tracks, he reached the cave – and found his companions lying dead. At that very moment a blood-curdling hiss made him spin round and he beheld the fearsome dragon rearing its head to strike. Like lightning, Cadmus seized a huge rock and hurled it at the beast, but the dragon's scales were harder than stone and the blow left it unharmed. However, this setback did not discourage Agenor's son for a single instant. Seizing his spear, he drove it between the scales and into the monster's spine. And then all hell broke loose. The hideous creature writhed in agony, hurling itself upon the rocks and scattering them far and wide. It thrashed the trees with its tail, snapping them like dry twigs. Cadmus sprang from one side to the other to avoid the rears and plunges of the dragon, till finally the opportunity he sought presented itself and he thrust his sword with awesome strength through the raging beast's throat, pinning it to a huge old oak tree. For all its massive trunk and towering height the tree crashed to the ground as the monster writhed in its death struggles, but Cadmus jumped nimbly aside and escaped unharmed. Suddenly, all was still. The fearful dragon was dead at last.

**THE FIGHT WITH THE DRAGON**

11

The brave young man could not believe his eyes when he saw what an awesome beast he had slain. He stood in wonder for a while, then finally took water and went to carry out the sacrifice alone. When it was done, he lifted his arms towards the sky and cried:

"I cannot tell, but surely some god lent me the strength to kill this monster, for no man could have done a deed like this unaided. To that unknown god I give thanks from the depths of my heart."

**CADMUS AND ATHENA**

Hardly were these words out of his mouth when Athena, goddess of wisdom, appeared before him.

"The gods help those who help themselves," the blue-eyed goddess told him. "This great feat was yours alone. Only, be warned that this dragon was a son of Ares, god of war, and perhaps a day will come when he will make you pay for the killing, justified though it was. But now, listen closely. Go and pull out the dragon's teeth, one by one, and sow them in the earth. Do what I tell you without delay, and do not ask me why."

As soon as she had said these words, the goddess disappeared.

Cadmus had no idea why he should perform such a pointless task, yet he did as the goddess had commanded. However, he had hardly finished sowing the dragon's teeth when some strange gleaming shoots began to appear in the soil which he had planted. It soon became clear that these shoots were none other than the tips of war lances slowly pushing their way out of the ground. Before long, the crests of helmets appeared beside the spears, then the heads of warriors, and finally, fully-armed fighting men emerged whole from the earth, shields on their arms and swords at their sides. At the sight of this new foe which had sprung up before his eyes Cadmus made as if to draw his sword, but his hand was not half way to the sheath when one of the warriors cried out:

**THE SPARTOE**

"Leave your sword in its place, son of Agenor. Others will fight for you."

And with these words a savage battle broke out among the earth-sprung warriors. Swords and lances clashed furiously, and one by one the warriors fell dead upon the very soil which had so recently given them birth.

Only five men survived that murderous struggle, and they were the most valiant of them all. Giving their hands in friendship they bowed the knee to Cadmus and swore eternal loyalty and devotion to him. These were the Spartoe, which means in Greek 'the sown men', and they received their name because they had sprung from the dragon's teeth which Cadmus had planted.

With the help of the Spartoe the son of Agenor built the fortress of Cadmea, and beneath it he founded Thebes, the city which has borne this name ever since.

Cadmus proved a wise and popular king. He taught his people to love the fine arts and he gave them their first alphabet, which they called 'Cadmean' after the king who taught it.

He governed and administered his kingdom well, making just laws and reigning in peace, with neither wars nor conquests. This peace, and the well-being of his people, were safeguarded by a powerful army led by the valiant Spartoe, who had sprung from the dragon's teeth.

**CADMUS AND HARMONIA**

Cadmus married the lovely Harmonia, daughter of Aphrodite, goddess of beauty and love, and their wedding was an unforgettable occasion, graced by the presence and the rich gifts of all the gods. It is said that on the very spot where the market place of Thebes was later built, the thrones of the Olympians had been placed for the wedding ceremony. Apollo himself honoured the bridal couple with the music of his lyre. And even today men point out the spot where the Muses sang their timeless song, 'Love what is fair, but never what is foul.'

Only two immortals were absent from the wedding: Ares, god of war, because Cadmus had slain his son, the dragon; and Eris, goddess of strife, because she could not bear the company of those who truly loved one another.

For it was not so much the splendour of the wedding that was memorable as the fact that in that moment gods and men united to join a couple who were themselves united by one of the greatest loves the world had ever seen.

Cadmus and Harmonia lived and reigned in joy and loving tenderness for many years, a model not only to Thebes but to the whole of Greece of what a marriage should be. 'May you always be as loving as Cadmus and Harmonia' was the wish on the lips of relatives and friends whenever a young couple got married in those times.

Yet if the love of Cadmus and Harmonia endured to the end, their happiness did not, for two of the four beloved daughters that were born to them, Semele and Ino, fell prey to the jealousy of the goddess Hera, and it cost them their lives.

14

Cadmus believed that these tragic deaths were somehow linked with Ares, who had never forgiven him for killing the dragon. And so he handed the throne of Thebes to his grandson Pentheus and set out with Harmonia for the far north, lest other misfortunes fall upon his descendants. But even in exile nothing but pain and bitterness awaited them, for there news came that their other grandson, Actaeon, had fallen a tragic victim to the wrath of the goddess Artemis, and all through no fault of his own.

Bitterly grieved to see how the gods had turned against him, Cadmus now remembered the words of Athena on the day he had slain the dragon: "Perhaps a day will come when you will pay for the killing, justified though it was."

"If this is the price I must pay for slaying Ares' dragon," he cried, "then I would rather be turned into such a creature myself than see my children and my children's children so cruelly punished!"

He had not even finished speaking when he felt his body growing thin and long and saw scales forming over his skin. His head became narrow and wedge-shaped, his tongue split in two and his manly voice shrank to a hiss. Cadmus had become a serpent!

In her despair and loneliness, Harmonia begged the gods to turn her into a snake as well, rather than be separated from her husband. And this they did.

**THE CUP OF PAIN**

And so the honour, the glory and the joy of their prime were matched by an old age filled with misery and pain. Transformed into two harmless snakes, Cadmus and Harmonia dragged their weary way among the rocks and stones. The couple who had once been the darlings of the gods were now despised by mortal and immortal alike. The son of Agenor and the daughter of Aphrodite, who had known such love and given it so generously, who had helped so many and never harmed a fly, were forced at last to drink the bitter dregs of sorrow and despair – and no one could tell the reason why. Only in death did the gods take pity on them, for their souls did not descend into the dark depths of Hades but travelled to the Fortunate Isles, where there is neither anguish nor regret.

Years went by and a man came northwards on a quest. His name was Illyrius and he was the youngest son of Cadmus and Harmonia, the child of their old age. Drawn by his love for his parents he had set out in search of their grave, but finding nothing he stayed and ruled in the land where they had died. And the country has been called Illyria ever since.

# ZETHUS AND AMPHION

Although Cadmus founded Thebes and built the fortress of Cadmea, it was two of his descendants, the twin brothers Zethus and Amphion, who built its fabled walls with their seven great gates.

The story of these two men and their mother, Antiope, is a strange and dramatic one.

Antiope was the daughter of Nycteus, king of Thebes, and such was her beauty that Zeus himself fell in love with her. Their union produced two sons, Zethus and Amphion, and their gripping tale begins before they were even born.

**ANTIOPE**

As soon as she felt the children stirring in her womb, Antiope trembled at the thought of her father's wrath. Always a daunting figure, anger made him a man to quail before.

So hard-hearted was Nycteus that not long before he had refused to give Antiope in marriage to Epopeus, the young king of Sicyon, simply because he wanted to keep his daughter to comfort his old age! What could Antiope tell him now – that the father of her children was Zeus himself? It was easy enough to say, but would he believe her, or would he kill her? And even if he did not kill her, would she not be disgraced for ever?

"Epopeus is the only person I can tell," said Antiope to herself. "He will understand and offer me protection."

And so Antiope stole out of her father's home secretly in the night and after a long and tiring journey she arrived in Sicyon.

Epopeus received her joyfully and married her at once. Now, Antiope could give birth to her children without fearing anybody.

But the young couple had hardly got over their joy at being reunited when a messenger came running into the palace gasping:

"It's the Theban army, with Nycteus at their head, and his brother Lycus. They've crossed the Isthmus of Corinth and they're headed here, for Sicyon!"

**NYCTEUS AND EPOPEUS FIGHT TO THE DEATH**
Epopeus immediately readied himself to face the king of Thebes. Antiope tried in vain to hold him back, begging him to hand her over to Nycteus instead.

"I would rather be taken from you, yet know you live, than mourn your death, my beloved!" she cried.

Ignoring Antiope's pleas, Epopeus challenged her cruel father to single combat. And both of them were slain. Then Lycus led the Theban troops into the city, carried off Antiope and returned to Thebes to become king.

But the new queen, Dirce, was an evil woman and her heart was filled with hatred for Antiope.

"Listen, Lycus," she warned her husband, "nobody must learn Antiope is with child, for if the truth be known, we shall never be sure that Thebes is safely in our grasp."

"Then what do you propose?" enquired the king.

"Hand her over to me," was the wicked queen's reply. "I know how to deal with her!"

Dirce locked Antiope in a gloomy dungeon, and within its dank walls the young woman gave birth to Zethus and Amphion, the sons of Zeus.

As soon as Dirce learned that the children had been born she snatched them cruelly from their mother, shut them in a basket and called the king's most trusty servant.

"Take these brats," she ordered, "climb Mount Cithaeron, and leave them on the bleakest, most deserted slope you find. I'm not asking you to kill them – let the gods decide whether they should live or not. I want no charge of murder laid at my door."

These words were sheer hypocrisy, of course. For Dirce was perfectly sure that once the babies were exposed on the mountainside it would not be long before they died or were eaten by wolves.

Having dealt with the infants, Dirce then ordered another servant to shackle Antiope in heavy chains and double bar the door of her cell so she would never be able to escape.

Yet Zeus could not abandon his children, and so, carefully though Dirce had chosen her servant for that task, the lord of the gods poured the spirit of mercy and justice into the man's soul. His eyes were opened to the cruelty of his mistress and he was overcome with pity for Antiope's defenceless babies. High on the slopes of Cithaeron he found a kind shepherd and confessed to him that he had been ordered by queen Dirce to leave the children to die, on the mountainside. When he heard these words,

the shepherd felt so sorry for the young things that he willingly agreed to take them and bring them up as his own children.

"Now my mind is at rest," said the servant, "for I am sure that I have left these helpless creatures in the hands of a kind and honest man. Know that their mother is Antiope, daughter of king Nycteus and wife of king Epopeus of Sicyon, who killed each other in single combat."

"But where is Antiope now?" asked the shepherd.

"I should not tell you this," replied the servant, "for though I have seen many injustices and held my tongue, this last was more than I could bear. Antiope is locked in an underground dungeon and not even allowed to see the light of day, though she has done nothing to deserve such a fate. But the worst of it is this: her children were torn from her arms and she believes that they are lost for ever now. I beg you, good shepherd, for my sake: keep my secret. Everything I have told you must remain between the two of us. Promise me that the children will never learn who their mother was."

When the servant had been given the promise he sought, he returned to Thebes and told the queen that her orders had been carried out and that by now the babies must have been devoured by wolves. And Dirce was delighted.

**ZETHUS AND AMPHION GROW UP ON CITHAERON**

But all the while the children were growing up on Cithaeron in the care of the kind shepherd. He fed them on goat's milk and mountain honey, taught them to call him 'father' and named them Zethus and Amphion. And when they were old enough to

begin to understand such things, he told them that their mother had been carried off by bandits and he no longer knew if she were alive or dead.

Up there in the hills, Zethus and Amphion grew into fine young men. Although they were twins, and one might have expected them to be very much alike, in fact they developed into two completely different individuals. Zethus became broad-shouldered and powerful, a truly heroic figure of a man. He loved hunting, and not even the most ferocious prey could make him quail. Amphion, by contrast, was musical and poetic. He would lead the flocks out to graze by the notes of his lyre, then sit on the mountain slopes for hours on end, playing and singing. So lovely were his melodies that they touched the hearts of the birds that heard them and tamed the savage spirits of the wildest beasts. Such was the power of Amphion's art that it could move the very stones around him.

Yet however much the young men differed, in one respect they were very much alike: in kindness of heart. Not only did they love each other dearly, but were united in affection for the shepherd they believed to be their father.

Twenty years had now gone by. And while Zethus and Amphion had grown up into fine young men, Antiope was still languishing in her vile prison and Dirce continued to enjoy the royal privileges she thought were hers for ever.

But in fact the wheel of time had turned full circle at last. For Zeus had never forgotten that in the end he must help his children, and that the throne of Thebes was theirs by right. And so one day, without any warning, the heavy bars fell from the door of Antiope's dungeon, it opened of its own accord, and the shackles dropped from her **ANTIOPE IS SET FREE**

wrists. The twins' mother was finally free.

Bewildered, she staggered to her feet, went over to the door and peered nervously out. There was not a soul in sight. This gave her the courage she needed, and with all the strength her frail limbs could command, backed by the power lent to her by hope, she fled straight to Cithaeron to hide from the avenging fury of Dirce. And what should happen but that her wild flight brought her to the very place where her children lived!

The shepherd was alone in the hut. She begged his help, revealed who she was and told him of her dreadful sufferings. Soon Zethus and Amphion came. The poor shepherd struggled to control his feelings, for he knew that before him an unhappy mother stood face to face with her lost children without knowing who they were. But he said nothing. Long ago he had given his promise, and now he must keep it. "Who knows what new ills may fall on Thebes if I reveal my secret?" the shepherd said to himself – and at that very moment a furious queen Dirce burst into the hut.

"Vile wretch!" she screamed. "Prison was the home the gods condemned you to. The time has come for you to die!"

**A TERRIBLE COMMAND**     And she immediately ordered Zethus and his brother to tie Antiope to the horns of a wild bull and let it tear her to pieces.

"She is guilty of hideous crimes," the queen went on. "I should have had her put to death long ago instead of keeping her in prison. She thought she could escape, but see how the gods have brought me to her and placed her in my hands and given me two fine young lads like you to punish her as she deserves."

## REUNITED AT LAST

Zethus and Amphion looked at their feet and said nothing.

"Move!" screeched Dirce. "Do you not hear me? The queen of Thebes commands you. Do as I say! Obey my command – for it is the will of the gods as well!"

With heavy hearts, the twins laid reluctant hands on the unknown woman who was their mother, not knowing how they could avoid the vile deed. But as they did so, the shepherd jumped to his feet crying:

"Miserable boys! Do you know who you have been ordered to kill? Your own mother, the former princess of Thebes!"

"Lies!" shrieked Dirce, but by way of answer the shepherd opened a trunk and took out the basket in which the boys had been brought to Cithaeron. The tiny garments they had worn were still inside.

"My sons!" sobbed Antiope, and rushed to embrace them.

"Treason!" hissed Dirce, turning on her heel.

"My troops will deal with this!"

But there was strength in the old shepherd yet, and he seized her arm in a grip of steel, crying out to the two young men:

"Now it is I who command! Take this woman and inflict on her the punishment she ordered for an innocent – your mother!"

Then Zethus and Amphion seized Dirce and bound her to the horns of the bull. And she was torn to pieces.

When justice had been done, the shepherd turned to the twins and said:

"My sons, this is the last time I can call you by that name, for I am not your father. As for your real father, your mother can reveal his name to you. The time has come for your return to Thebes, where the throne of Cadmus awaits you. Throw down the tyrant Lycus and set the city free. This is my final counsel as the father you believed me all these years. Go now, with my blessing. I shall remain here. For here I was born, here I grew to manhood, here I have reached old age, and here I wish to die."

And so Zethus and Amphion took their mother and went down into the city, where they overthrew the tyrant Lycus and became kings of Thebes.

The first task which faced them there was the fortification of the town. Cadmus had built walls, but only for Cadmea, the upper city, on its defensive spur of rock, and since his day the town which lay at its feet had grown considerably. Now new walls were needed, to enfold the whole of Thebes within their circuit.

Zethus and Amphion buckled down to the task. But just as they were unalike in other ways, so their methods of building differed immensely. Zethus used his titanic strength to heave huge boulders into place with his bare hands, but Amphion built in a strange and very different fashion. He simply played his lyre. And they say that such was the power of his music that the stones lifted themselves, at its command and fell into place, row upon row. Thus, with strength of hand and magic notes, the two brothers raised the mighty walls of the city which came to be known as Seven-Gated Thebes, after the seven tall gateways set in its impregnable circuit.

Zethus and Amphion ruled over the city in harmony and brotherly love, but they were not destined to live out their days in happiness.

Zethus married Aedon, and they had one child, a boy. But later, Aedon went mad and killed her child. Afterwards, she mourned for it ceaselessly, night and day, until at last the cruel loss of her son was more than she could bear and she died of grief. The gods took pity on her and transformed her into a nightingale and ever afterwards, Zethus awoke at dawn to the sad and lonely song of a bird.

Amphion married Niobe, the daughter of Tantalus. They lived in happiness for many years and produced fourteen children, and yet...

But that brings us to the last and one of the most tragic stories in this volume: the myth of Niobe.

# N I O B E

The tale of Niobe is not only the most dramatic but perhaps the most daring in the whole of Greek mythology. For like the myths of Prometheus and Deucalion's Flood it poses a very bold and direct question: why are the gods so often unjust to mortals?

Niobe may have been at fault, but she was punished so harshly and inhumanly that whatever crime she was guilty of pales before the vengeance that was wreaked on her. The sentence passed on Niobe becomes a condemnation of the gods themselves.

As the wife of Amphion and the mother of so many children, Niobe was the happiest woman in the world – until the day disaster struck. She was a queen, her husband loved her dearly, but above all she had her fourteen children, seven boys and seven girls, all as fair as young gods and the pride and joy of her heart.

**THE HAPPIEST OF WOMEN**

Niobe's children were her whole existence. She washed and combed them with her own hands, fed the younger ones, and rejoiced in the handsome and united family she and her husband had brought into the world.

To be proud of one's family is no crime – as long as one does not make hurtful comparisons. But in her pride, Niobe did make such a comparison, and in so doing she insulted no less a person than a goddess.

"I am the best and happiest mother on earth," Niobe would often say. "Not only on earth, but in the heavens, too." Until one day her old nurse said to her:

"But, madam, the story our parents and our grandparents always told us was that the best and happiest of mothers is the goddess Leto, who bore Apollo and Artemis, both mighty gods respected by mortals and immortals alike."

**FATAL PRIDE** "I have borne fourteen such children," was Niobe's proud response. "My sons are a match for the finest athletes, and brilliant horsemen. My daughters are the fairest flowers of Thebes, and the seven great towers of the city walls bear their names. So how could Leto, with a mere two children, be a better mother than me?"

"You may be queen," the nurse replied, "but once you were just a child at my breast, and that gives me the right to chide you. Take those words back! Be as proud as you like among mortals, but be humble before the gods. For their power is beyond all reckoning, and we are as nothing beside them."

"Others are nothing, perhaps, but not I."

"Madam, watch your tongue!"

"I am the darling of the gods, and my fourteen children give me my power. My shield is my husband, king of Thebes and son of Zeus!"

"Alas, my lady, if only the gods could not hear the words of mortals and read their thoughts, then perhaps no harm would come to you. But now I am afraid, very afraid. I fear disaster, madam."

Sure enough, Leto did learn what Niobe had said, and her rage was terrible to see. **THE ANGER** She immediately summoned the soothsayer Manto, daughter of the prophet Tiresias, **OF THE GODDESS** and commanded her:

"Go now to Thebes and order the mothers of the city to make humble sacrifice to me. And be sure that not a single one of them fails to pay heed, for the vengeance that will fall on her will be hideous beyond all imagining."

Manto hastened to Thebes and proclaimed the goddess' command in every corner of the city, and below the palace walls as well. As soon as they heard her words every mother in the town hastily offered sacrifice to Leto. All except Niobe, who remained stubbornly in the palace.

"Go, your majesty," the old nurse begged. "Go before disaster sfrikes. Go now, for soon it will be too late!"

"I do not fear Leto," was the queen's reply. "I have never humbled myself before, and I shall not do so now. I have fourteen children and I am the better mother. I'll offer no sacrifice to her!" And she did not.

Then Leto called her children to her, the two unerring archers Apollo and Artemis, and in a voice trembling with rage she told them of the terrible insult she had been subjected to. And then she added:

"If Niobe is not punished, men will cease to revere me, and I shall no longer be worshipped as a goddess. My altars will be left to crumble and I shall go unheeded by the other gods."

"Fear not, mother," was Apollo's reply. "We shall allow no mortal woman to humiliate you, whoever she may be. We know what you seek of us, and we shall carry out the deed."

"Come, brother!" cried Artemis, "and we shall see how many children that upstart has left to her name before very long. We'll teach her to insult a goddess – especially our mother!"

The pair of them set off for Thebes at once, their quivers bristling with the deadly arrows which warned of the catastrophe to come.

When they reached the city, all the young men of Thebes were taking part in athletics contests at the foot of the castle walls. And in every event, Niobe's seven fine sons stood out from the other competitors.

**AN INHUMAN REVENGE**

Wrapped in a concealing cloud, Apollo seated himself on a rock high up on the acropolis. His keen eye soon made out Niobe's seven sons. Next, he took seven arrows from his quiver and laid them at his side. Then, after another careful look at the stadium below, he picked up an arrow and took aim. The missile winged its way

earthwards with a shrill whine, followed by Apollo's steady gaze. And it found its mark: one of the athletes fell lifeless to the ground. Then he took another arrow, and a third, and a fourth, until seven fine young men lay stretched out dead in the dust.

And so, in the hour when victors should be praised, the people of Thebes found themselves mourning their dead, and instead of a procession led by laurel-crowned champions, a funeral cortege made its solemn way to the palace, bearing the bodies of the city's seven finest youths.

As they came up the hill, Amphion stood waiting at the castle gate, as he always did, to offer his congratulations to the victors. But the procession which approached him now was like no other he remembered. He gazed in growing anxiety as the long column drew nearer, silent and mournful. Thoughts of some dreadful disaster were already turning over in his mind, but none so dreadful as that which greeted him as he saw laid out before him on the ground, one by one, the bodies of all his seven sons.

Amphion's eyes beheld the sight, but for a long moment his mind could not take it in. And when at last he had fully comprehended the horror of what lay before him, he raised his eyes to the heavens and a silent cry of anguish tore his heart asunder.

## HAVE PITY, MIGHTY GODDESS!

Then his head dropped, his eyes fired with despairing wrath and his hand went to his sword-hilt. A moment later, with dreadful suddenness, he plunged the blade into his own breast.

As Amphion sank lifeless to the ground, Niobe and her seven daughters appeared in the gateway. With heartrending cries of grief the girls threw themselves on the bodies of their murdered brothers and their beloved father.

Only Niobe remained standing. Unable to bear the hideous sight, she hid her head in her hands. Although she managed to hold back the sobs which were choking her, she could not prevent the tears from streaming down her face. She saw that the disaster they had warned her of had struck, and an agonizing struggle was now taking place inside her. For even this inhuman punishment could not bow the queen's proud spirit. In her heart of hearts she could never accept that Leto was a better mother than she, or that by this blow she had established her superiority.

And so, drawing on whatever reserves of courage were left within her, Niobe wiped the tears from her cheeks, lifted her arms heavenwards and cried:

"Leto! May your soul rejoice in the hideous crime you have committed. Let it exult in the triumph of your cruelty – but do not think this is a victory, Leto. However many lifeless corpses lie scattered around me, I still have my seven daughters to sweeten my sorrow. Oh yes, I have always been a better mother than you, and I still am. You shall never be my equal!"

All who heard Niobe froze at her words. Blinded by her pride, could she not see that her rash cry was yet another challenge to the goddess, and one that would surely not go unanswered? And a moment later the shrill whine of an arrow drew their eyes like a magnet towards one of Niobe's daughters: transfixed by the deadly shaft, she was already gasping out her life above her brother's body. For now Artemis had taken up where Apollo had laid down his bow. One by one, her swift, sure arrows tore into the hearts of Niobe's daughters. Six of the seven already lay dead and now only one was left – little Chloris, the youngest and dearest of the unhappy queen's beloved daughters.

In this last moment, surrounded by the heartrending evidence of the gods' inconceivable harshness, Niobe's pride collapsed. Wild with grief, she threw herself on her knees, turned her eyes heavenwards and cried out in a voice broken with anguish:

"O great and mighty Leto! You have defeated me! Forgive me for insulting you, take pity on my misery, and, I beg you, I implore you: let me keep the last of my little ones to soften my grief!"

Niobe writhed in her misery. Again and again she threw herself to the ground, stretching her hands towards the heavens and beating her breast in supplication.

"If you cannot take pity on me, at least show mercy on this harmless creature. Kill

me, but let her live: to cry, to forget, to bow her knee before your mighty name!"

Niobe had now humbled herself utterly before Leto. The last shreds of her self-esteem had fallen from her, and the goddess was delighted. But she was not moved to pity. Niobe's cries would have melted a heart of ice, but they did not soften Leto's rage. A brief and vicious whine rang through the air and the last of Artemis' arrows buried itself in the last of Niobe's daughters. She died in her mother's arms.

The queen stood among the gods' cruel handiwork a creature dazed with grief. All her children lay dead. Her husband, too. Even little Chloris. The slaughter was beyond belief, too terrible for words – but unalterably real. Her pride and happiness in ruins, Niobe no longer even had the strength to cry. Speechless and dry-mouthed, she remained there in her sorrow as if all life had fled from her body, and only the tears which flowed down her cheeks bore witness to her unendurable pain.

**THE GODS STILL THIRST FOR VENGEANCE** Then suddenly her ears were pierced by a hideous and rasping voice. The gods had not yet had their fill of revenge. The soothsayer Manto was making her rounds again, crying shrilly in every quarter of the city:

"Hear my words, people of Thebes! The immortal gods forbid you to bury the children of Niobe. To increase this vain woman's punishment and to teach every man and woman in this town the true might of the gods, the bodies of Niobe's children will go unburied and be eaten by the birds of prey."

Again and again the prophetess shrieked out her message, until Niobe could endure no more. The warm and living queen slowly turned into a block of stone. Soon, all that remained of her loving spirit were the tears that flowed from her stone eyes and the anguish which swelled within her stone heart.

And as that anguish swelled, so did the stone figure of Niobe, until it towered over the rooftops of Thebes, a looming accusation against the injustice of the immortals.

When the gods beheld that rising pillar of rock, and saw the tears which still flowed from Niobe's stone eyes to reproach them for their hideous revenge, they at last comprehended the evil they had done, and were filled first with shame and then with fear.

As if they knew now that theirs was no victory, but a humiliating defeat, they came secretly in the night and buried Niobe's children with their own hands. And then, raising a fearful whirlwind, they lifted the rock and bore it far away into the depths of Asia, where they hid it behind Mount Sipylus in the hope that the cruel act they had committed might thus be forgotten.

But it was not forgotten. Thousands of years have gone by and men still recount the myth of Niobe, for all the efforts of the gods to hide their crime.

For it was not mere chance that gave birth to this tale.

**GRIEF TURNS NIOBE TO STONE**

**THE DEFEAT OF THE GODS**

On the far slopes of Mount Sipylus one can still see a rock which weeps with the melting of the snows, and bears some resemblance to a sorrowing woman. However, could such a rock alone have given rise to a myth like this? Perhaps some terrible disaster really did befall the royal house of Thebes, a disaster which provoked a universal outrage which in its turn gave birth to the myth. From then on it is merely a question of imagination and reasoning – but logical and bold reasoning, so bold that it places mortals and immortals, Mankind and Olympians, in opposing camps. For here the gods are judged, and found guilty of a crime so monstrous it outreaches the powers of justice; while mortal men, in the person of Niobe, raise up against it the strong rock built of all their sufferings, a rock so enduring it can outlast the gods themselves.

For whatever else may be true, this much is certain: Somewhere on the face of this earth there is such a rock, shaped like a tragic but still proud woman who seems to be sending heavenwards a mute yet eloquent cry of accusation. Try as they might, storms and tempests cannot muffle this cry, and neither can the passing of the centuries.

And on Olympus? Up there, there is nothing. Nothing but bare and silent crags, scoured by the icy winds. The halls of the gods are as if they had never been.

# SOME ANSWERS TO POSSIBLE QUERIES

To those of our readers, young or old, whose reading of this mythology series may have prompted certain questions, we would like to say the following:

It is possible that you may have read the same myth elsewhere and noticed significant differences. This does not necessarily mean that one version is right and the other wrong. In their retelling, myths came to differ widely from place to place and from age to age and as a result several version's are now extant. In this work, we decided to give one version only, choosing either that most widely accepted, or the one we felt to have the most value. Working by the same criteria we have often added materials taken from other sources to round out a myth.

Another frequent cause of bewilderment are the contradictions generally encountered in mythology. For example, in one myth Zeus may be depicted as kind and fair, and in another tyrannical and unjust. Even Homer does much the same thing in the Iliad. At one point he has Thersites, a common soldier, lashing Agamemnon himself with the tongue of truth, while at another we see him crying like a child beneath the blows of Odysseus' gilded sceptre. These apparent contradictions must be accepted at face value, for it must not be forgotten that while sceptred monarchs had the right to command, the story-teller's lyre was in the hands of the common people, and clashes were inevitable. It is significant that while rulers are depicted as being the equals of Ares in power and daring, the singer-poets did not create a single myth in which the god of war emerges victorious, but many in which he suffers defeat and humiliation.

As for the illustrations, we believe that a picture should speak for itself. Nevertheless, we should like to say a few words about them.

We had to choose between two schools of thought. According to the one —and this is a line taken by many illustrators— we would have been obliged to remain faithful to the classical originals, chiefly vase-paintings, working in two dimensions, without perspective and with sparing use of colour. The other approach dictated that we use a modern style, and this we have preferred — but with one important prerequisite: that the picture, like the text, must itself be mythology. Thus, while keeping to the classical line, we have added a few elements of perspective where this seemed absolutely necessary. In one respect, however, we felt that we must have absolute freedom, and that was in the colouring. In our opinion, it was precisely the bright colours we have used which would give our work the fairytale air which the myths have to the modern reader's eye. For the ancients, in contrast, mythology was religion. For them the gods were real and not mythical beings. To us mythology is something else — a collection of wise and charming stories which shine like a bright fabric of the imagination from out of the depths of the centuries. It is for this reason that we have tried to illustrate this series with colour alone, or rather, by weaving harmonious contrasts of colour, but never forgetting that our theme is Greek mythology.